The Kew Gardens
BEAUTIFUL FLOWERS
COLOURING BOOK

Over 40 beautiful illustrations
plus colour guides

ARCTURUS

ROYAL BOTANIC GARDENS

All illustrations included in this book have been taken from the Library, Art & Archives Collections of the Royal Botanic Gardens, Kew.

Special thanks to everyone at Kew Publishing, Lynn Parker, Art and Illustrations Curator, and Dr Martyn Rix, Editor of *Curtis's Botanical Magazine*.

ARCTURUS

This edition published in 2016 by Arcturus Publishing Limited
26/27 Bickels Yard, 151–153 Bermondsey Street,
London SE1 3HA

ISBN: 978-78428-323-0
CH005241NT
Supplier 37, Date 0916, Print run 5560

Printed in Romania

Created for children 10+

Introduction

The artworks presented here are taken from the archive of *Curtis's Botanical Magazine*, the longest running periodical featuring colour illustrations of plants in the world. Founded in 1787 by apothecary and botanist William Curtis (1746–99), as *The Botanical Magazine*, it appealed to natural history scholars as well as ladies and gentlemen wanting information on the many newly introduced ornamental flowers that were in vogue in the gardens of the wealthy and fashionable. The 19th century saw a proliferation of plant collecting, with new species being sought out to satisfy the Victorian craze for the new and exotic.

Each issue of the magazine contained three hand-coloured, copper-engraved plates alongside the text, which described the Latin name, genus and qualities, along with the plant's botanical, horticultural and historical background, as well as associated information relating to what we might now call conservation, and any economic applications or uses.

Curtis charged one shilling per month and soon had 2,000 subscribers. Accomplished artists were commissioned to produce the plates, and the magazine was an instant success. The plates continued to be hand-coloured until 1948, when a scarcity of colourists led to the implementation of photographic reproduction.

The name of the magazine was changed to *Curtis's Botanical Magazine* after Curtis's death in 1799. It was first produced at Kew in 1841, when William Jackson Hooker (1785–1865) moved south from Glasgow University to become Director of the Royal Botanic Gardens. Joseph Dalton Hooker (1817–1911) took over the role of editor from his father in 1865, and the magazine has continued to be produced by Kew staff and artists to this day.

Most of the artworks included here are by Walter Hood Fitch (1817–92), who illustrated more than 2,700 plants for the magazine and published over 10,000 illustrations in total during his career. Six plates are painted by Matilda Smith (1854–1926), Kew's first official botanical artist, appointed in 1898. She contributed more than 2,300 plates to the magazine over a 40-year period, until 1923.

The plants illustrated in the magazine come from all over the world, collected by a vast array of plant collectors, described by their 'discoverers' who are designated as the authors of their respective plant names.

Presented in this compilation are 44 colour plates of plants together with their corresponding black-and-white lithographs for you to try your hand at colouring. The original watercolour drawings were made from life, so you can be sure that your finished renderings will be based on accurate and precise representations of the actual plants. A key to the plates, using plant names given at the time of publication, along with the names of their respective discoverers (authors) may be found in the next few pages.

Key: List of plates

1 *Lilium nepalense*
David Don

2 *Iris nudicaulis*
Jean-Baptiste Lamarck

3 *Gladiolus cruentus*
Thomas Moore

4 *Vanda cristata*
Nathaniel Wallich

5 *Sida integerrima*
William J Hooker

6 *Odontoglossum vexillarium*
Heinrich G. Reichenbach

7 *Cattleya schilleriana*
Heinrich G. Reichenbach

8 *Rhododendron fortunei*
John Lindley

9 *Columnea kalbreyeri*
Maxwell Masters

10 *Gardenia malleifera*
William J. Hooker

11 *Viola pedunculata*
John Torrey & Asa Gray

12 *Echinocactus cinnabarinus*
William J. Hooker

13 *Ipomaea pulchella*
Albrecht Wilhelm Roth

14 *Cereus extensus*
Joseph zu Salm-Reiffer-
scheidt-Dyck

15 *Magnolia campbellii*
Joseph Hooker

16 *Salvia leucantha*
Antonio José Cavanilles

17 *Stanhopea bucephalus*
John Lindley

18 *Dendrobium devonianum*
Joseph Paxton

19 *Tropaeolum speciosum*
Eduard Friedrich Poeppig
& Stephan Endlicher

20 *Cyclamen africanum*
Pierre Edmond Boissier &
Georges François Reuter

21 *Anguria warscewiczii*
William J. Hooker

22 *Coelogyne lagenaria*
John Lindley

23 *Tillandsia bulbosa*
William J. Hooker

24 *Vanda tricolor*
John Lindley

25 *Aquilegia alpina*
Carl Linnaeus

26 *Berberidopsis corralina*
Joseph Hooker

27 *Hibiscus grossulariifolius*
Friedrich Anton Wilhelm
Miquel

28 *Pittosporum flavum*
William J. Hooker

29 *Nolana lanceolata*
Michel Félix Dunal

30 *Saccolabium miniatum*
John Lindley

31 *Phalaenopsis mariae*
Frederick William
Thomas Burbidge

32 *Acacia hispidissima*
Augustin Pyramus de
Candolle

33 *Abelia floribunda*
Martin Martens & Henri
Guillaume Galeotti

34 *Amaryllis pardina*
Joseph Hooker

35 *Bejaria coarctata*
Aimé Jacques
Alexandre Bonpland

36 *Scutellaria cordifolia*
Gotthilf Heinrich Ernst
Muhlenberg

37 *Campanula strigosa*
Joseph Banks & Daniel
Solander

38 *Rosa alba* L.
Carl Linnaeus

39 *Billbergia euphemiae*
Charles Jacques
Edouard Morren

40 *Tulipa kaufmanniana*
Eduard August von
Regel

41 *Martynia fragrans*
John Lindley

42 *Camellia reticulata*
John Lindley

43 *Higginsia regalis*
William J. Hooker

44 *Puya altensteinii* var.
gigantea
Johann Heinrich
Friedrich Link, Johann
Friedrich Klotzsch &
Christoph Friedrich Otto

M.S.del,J.N.Fitch lith.

Vincent Brooks,Day&Son.Imp

W. Fitch, del. et lith.

Vincent Brooks, Day & Son, Imp.

5806.

W. Fitch, del. et lith.

Vincent Brooks, Day & Son, Imp.

3

W. Fitch, del. et lith.

Vincent Brooks, Day & Son, Imp

4304

Fitch del. et lith.

Reeve, imp

4304

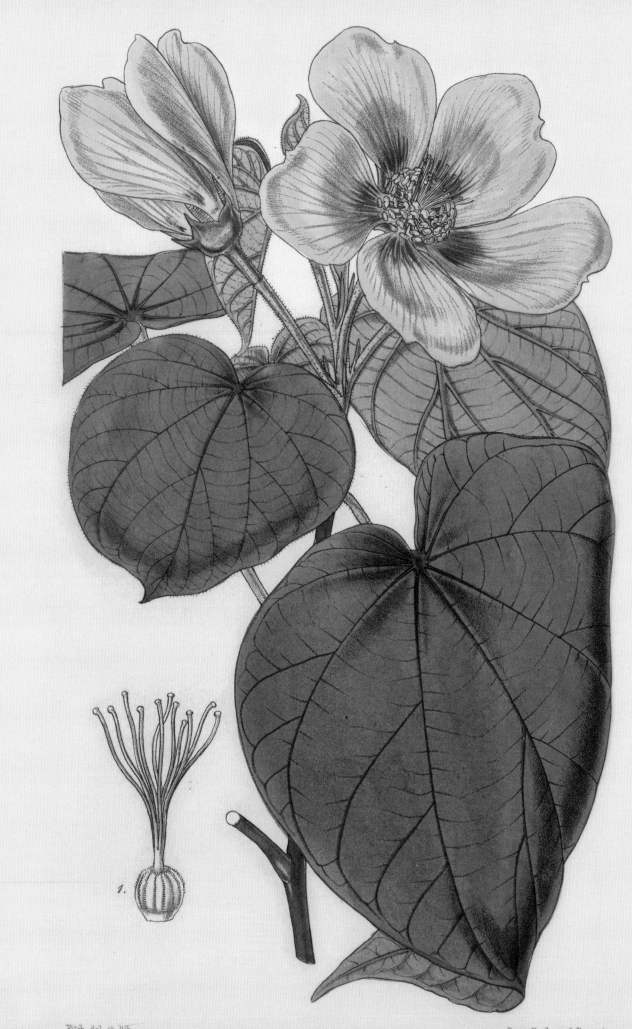

5

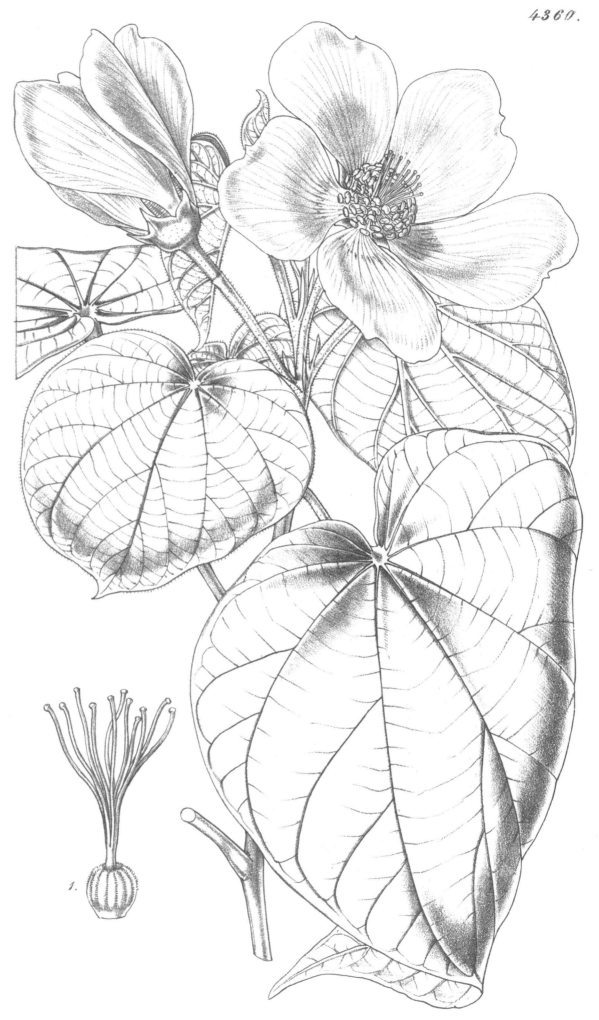

1.

Fitch, del et lith.

Reeve, Benham & Reeve, imp.

W.Fitch, del et lith

Vincent Brooks Day & Son, Imp

W. Fitch, del et lith.

Vincent Brooks, Imp.

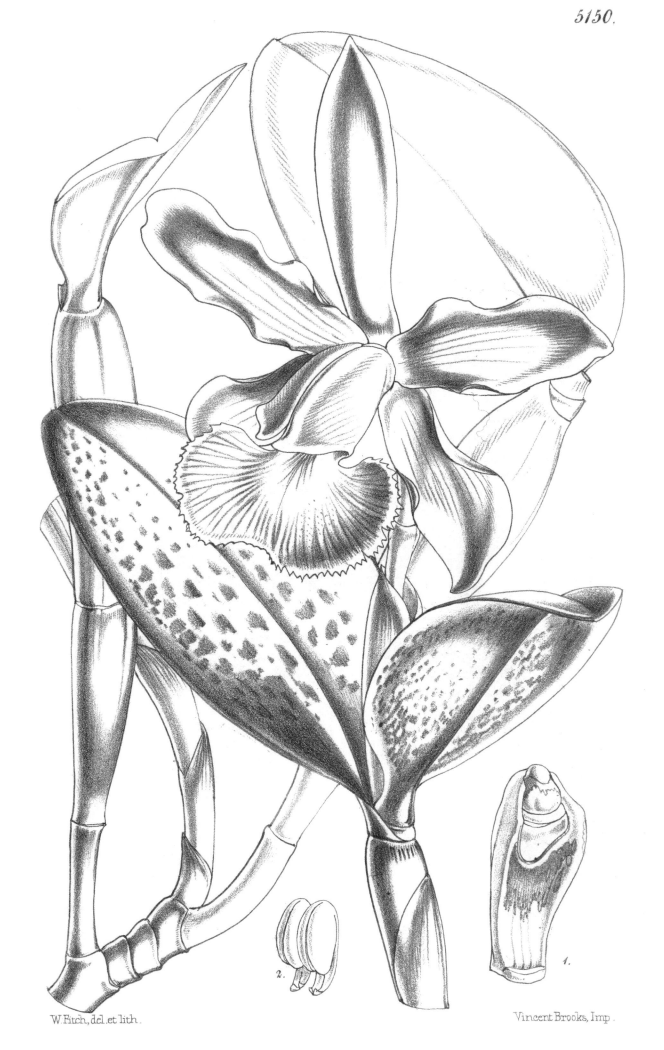

W.Fitch, del.et lith.   Vincent Brooks, Imp.

1.

2.

3.

4307

Fitch del & lith

Reeve, imp

4307

Fitch del & lith.

Reeve, imp.

5004.

W.Fitch del.et lith.

Vincent Brooks Imp

5004.

W.Fitch del.et lith.

Vincent Brooks Imp.

Fitch, del. et lith.

Reeve, imp.

4305

Fitch del. et lith.

Reeve, imp.

4305

W. Fitch del.ᵗ

Pub by S. Curtis Glazenwood Essex Feb.ᵗ 1.1844

Swan Sc.

W. Fitch del.ᵗ   Pub by S. Curtis Glazenwood Essex Feb.ʳ 1.1844   Swan Sc.

15

M.S.del. J N Fitch lith

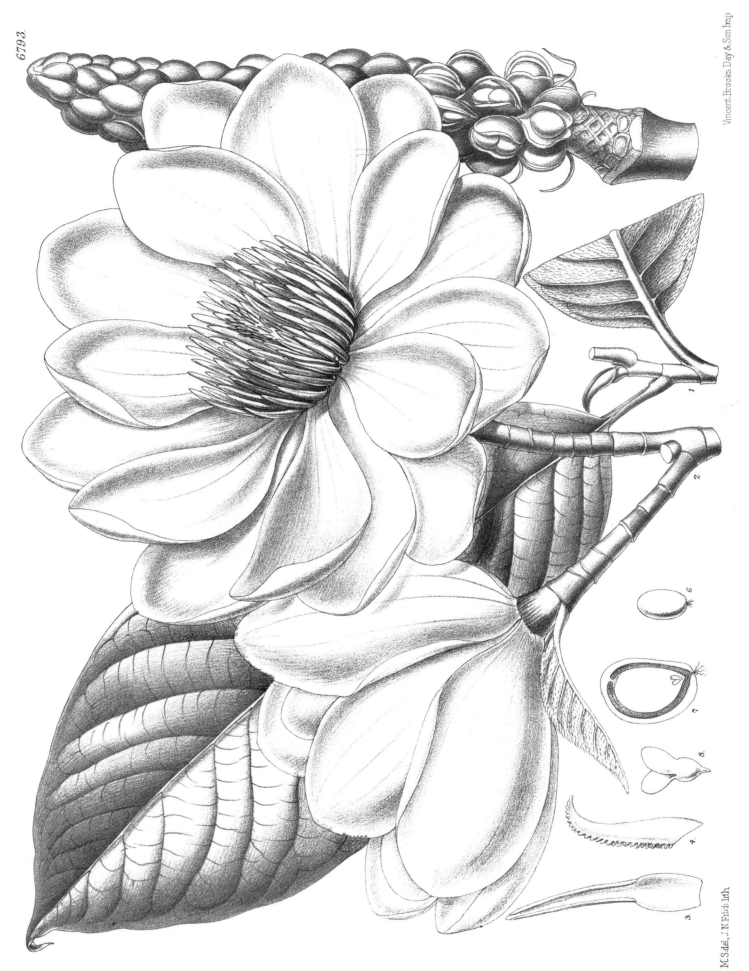

Vincent Brooks Day & Son Imp.

L. Reeve & C° London.

M.S.del, J.N.Fitch lith.

1.

3.

2.

Fitch del. et lith.

Reeve imp.

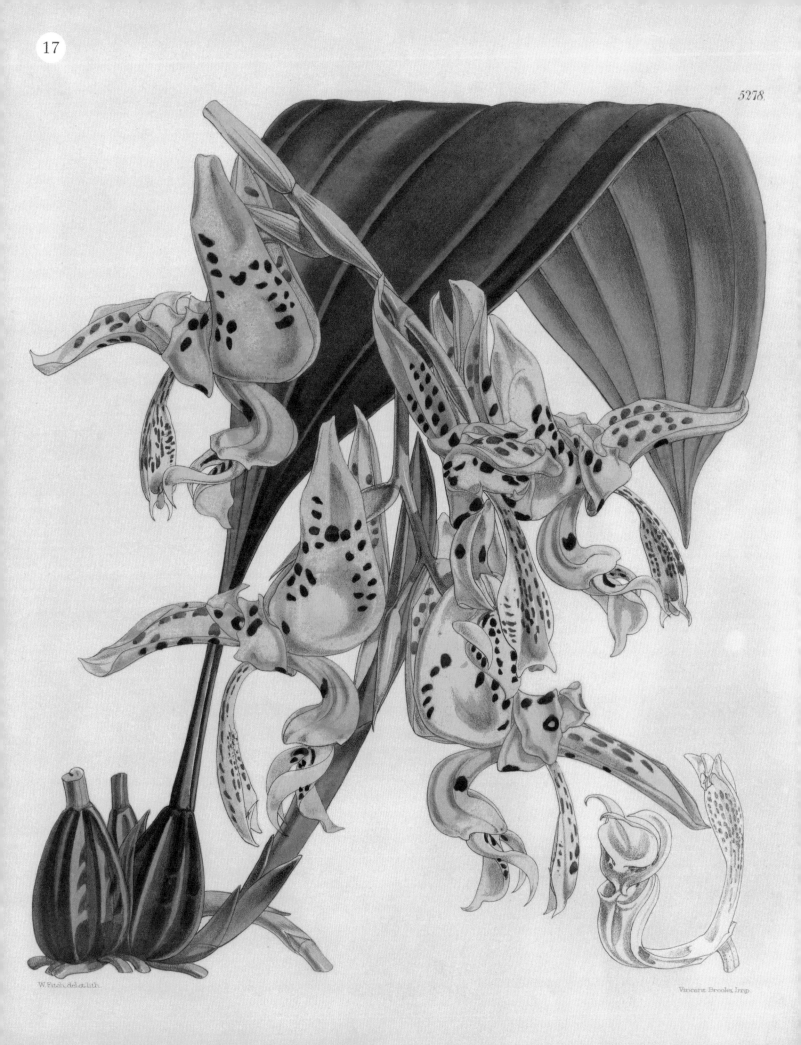

W. Fitch, del et lith.

Vincent Brooks, Imp.

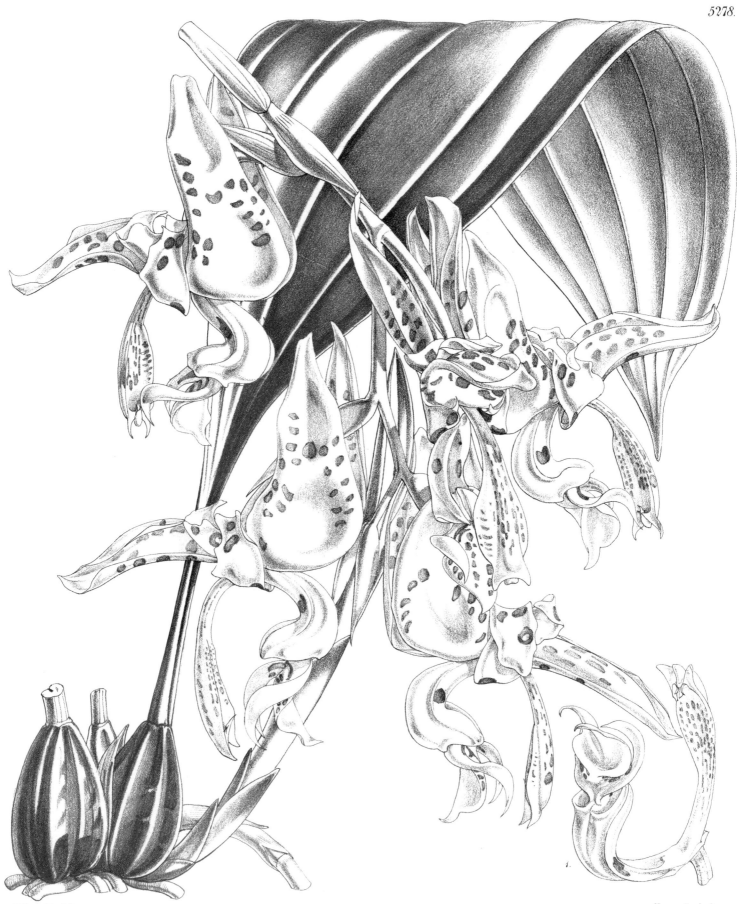

W. Fitch, del. et lith.

Vincent Brooks, Imp.

18

Fitch, del. et lith.

R. B. & R. imp.

1.

1.

Fitch, del. et lith.

Reeve, imp.

W. Fitch del et lith.

Vincent Brooks Day & Son Imp.

W. Fitch del et lith.

Vincent Brooks Day & Son Imp.

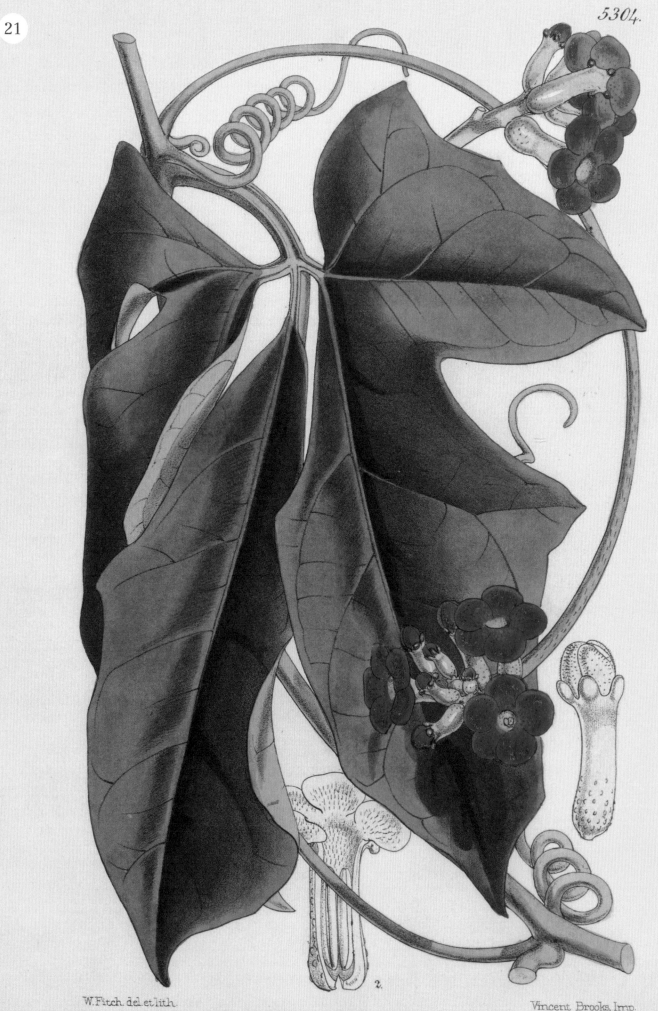

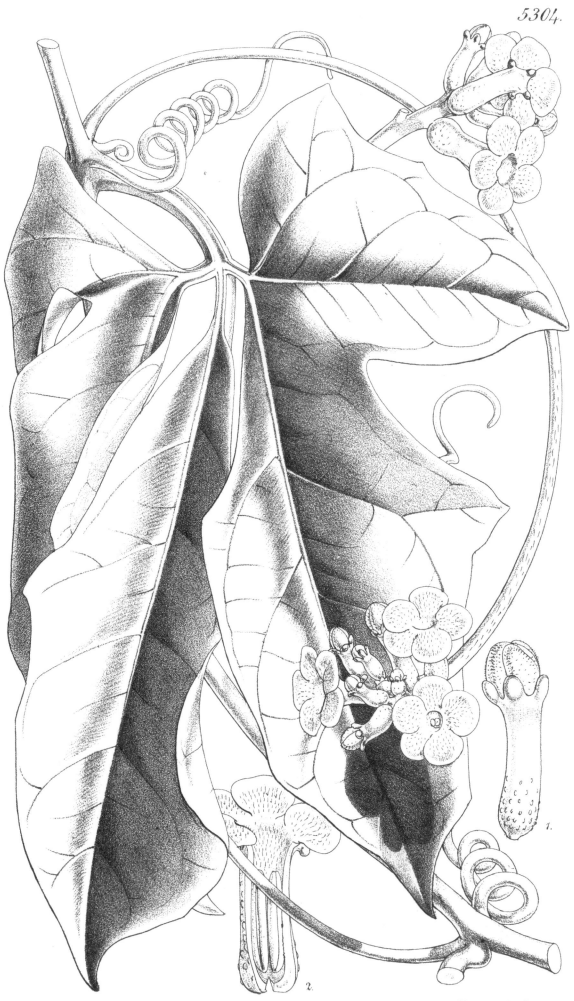

W. Fitch, del. et lith.

Vincent Brooks, Imp.

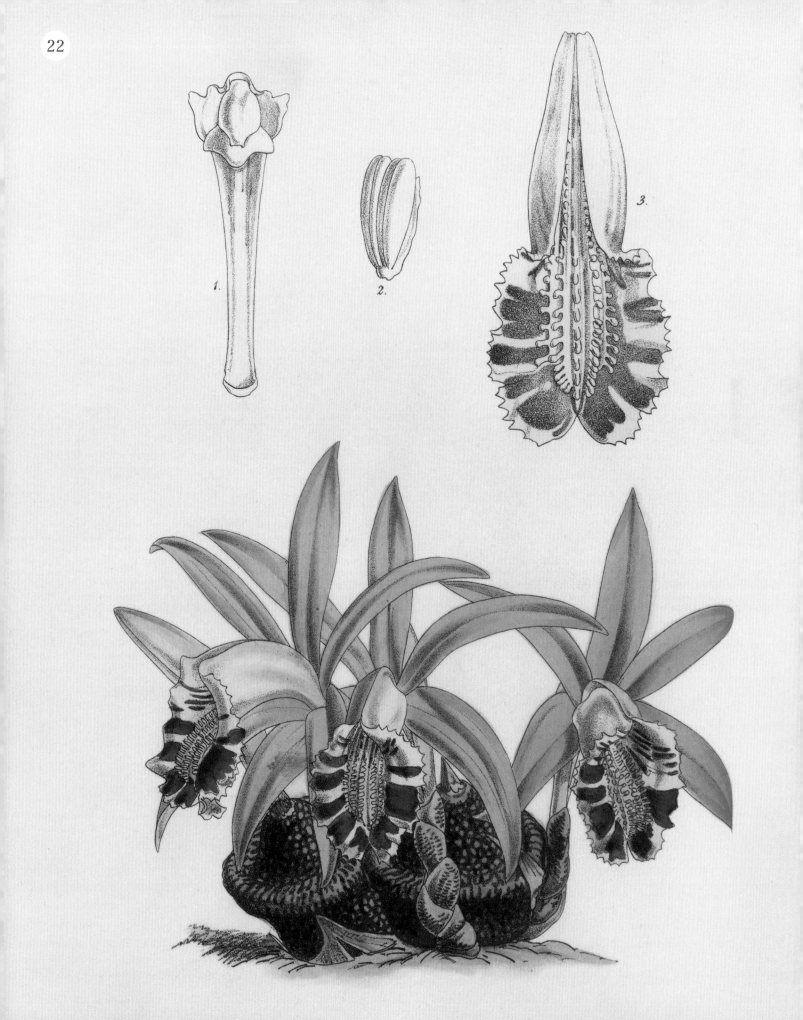

22

1.

2.

3.

W. Fitch, del. et lith.

Vincent Brooks, Imp.

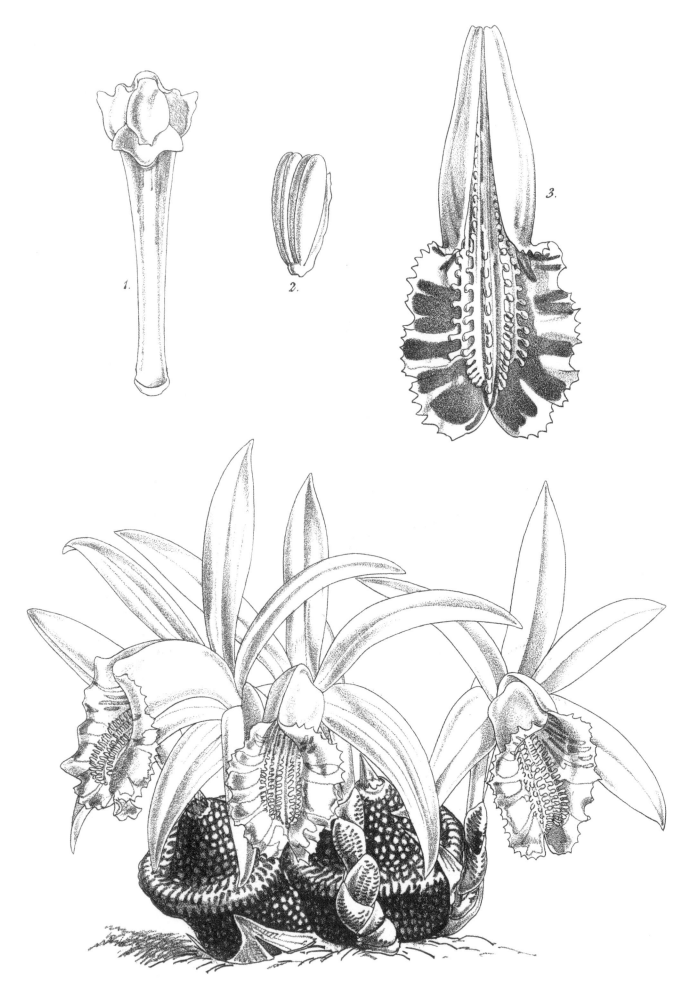

23

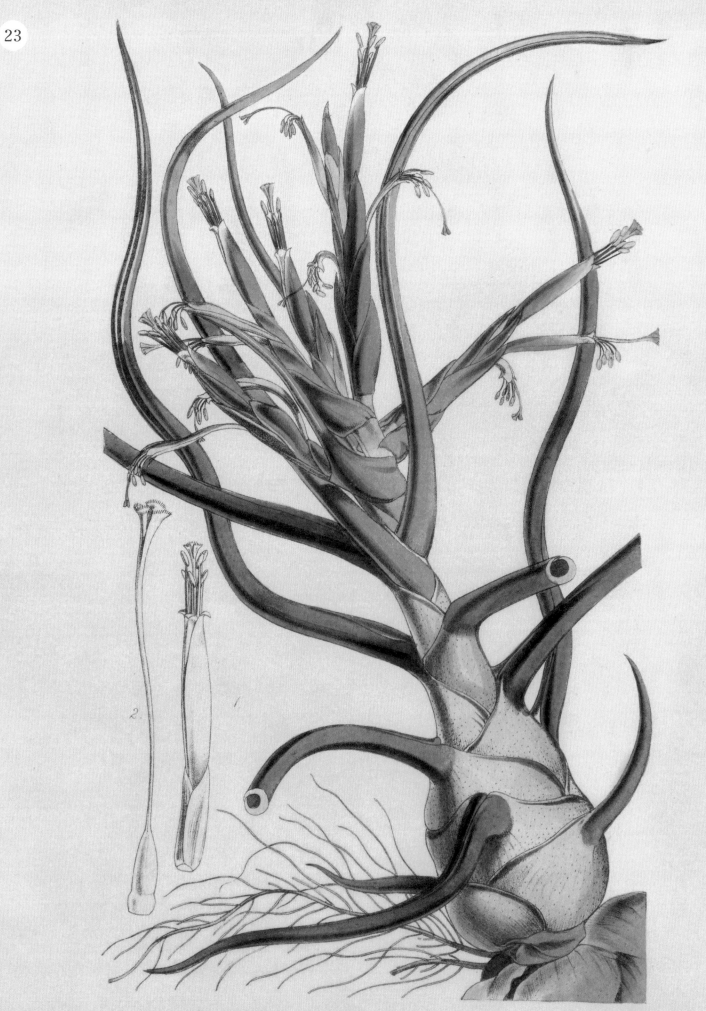

4288.

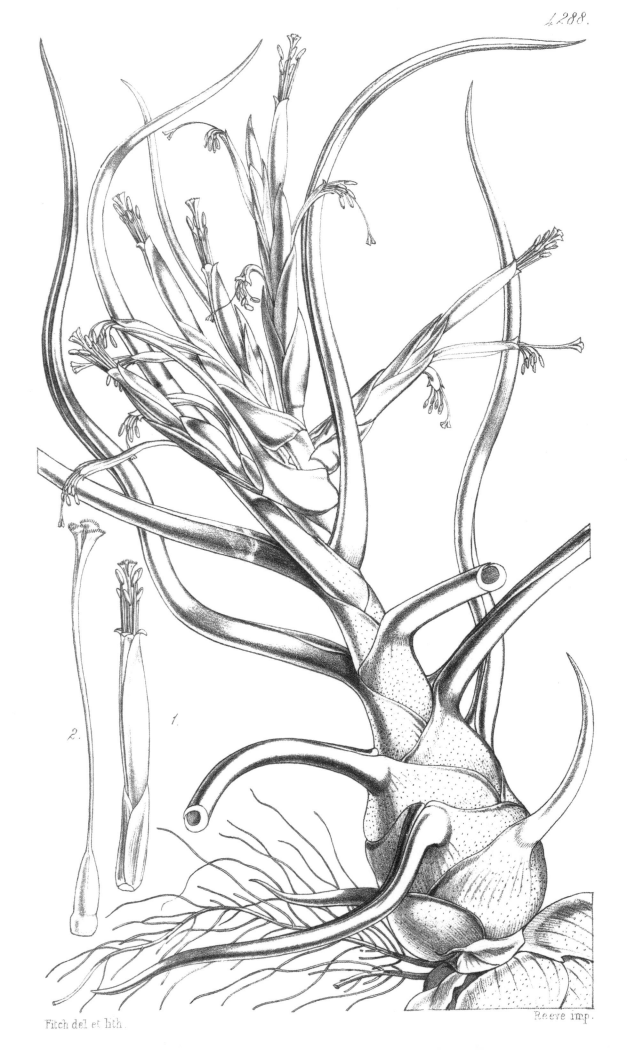

Fitch del et lith.

Reeve imp.

Fitch del. et lith.

Reeve, Benham & Reeve, imp.

4432.

Fitch del. et lith.

Reeve, Benham & Reeve, imp.

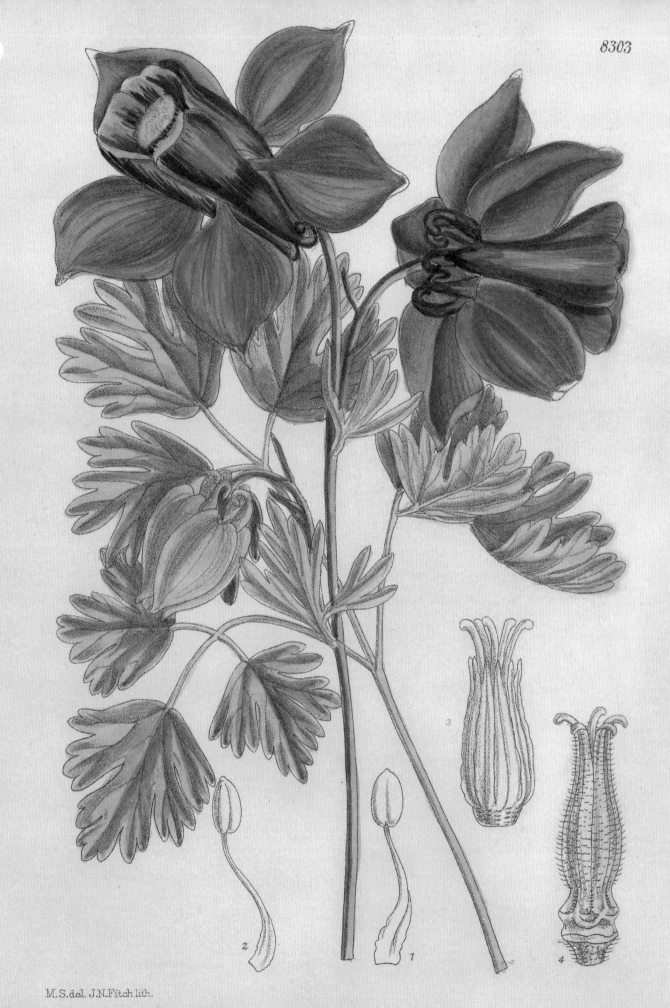

M.S.del. J.N.Fitch lith.

L Reeve & C°.London.

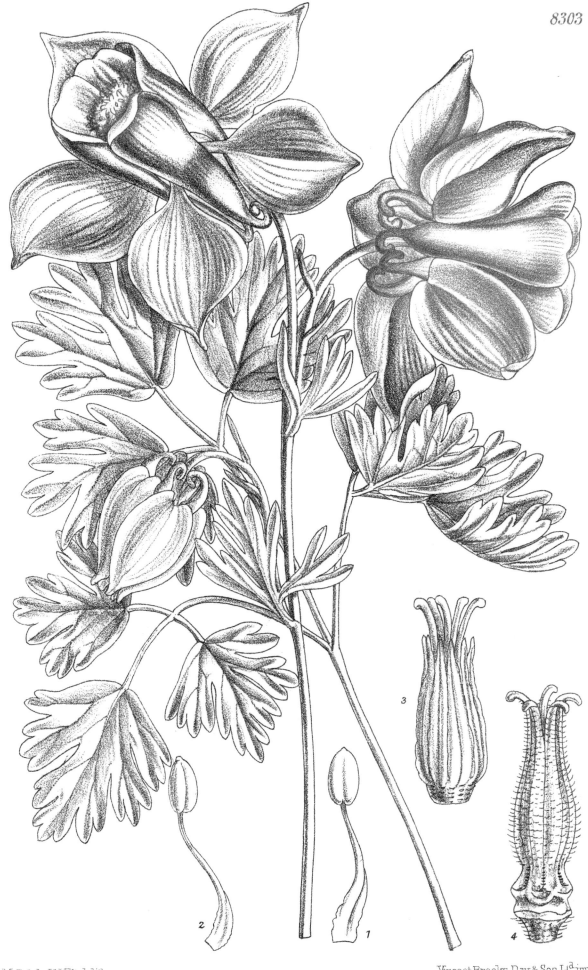

Vincent Brooks Day & Son Ltᵈ imp

L Reeve & Cᵒ London.

W. Fitch. del. et lith.

Vincent Brooks, Imp.

4329.

Fitch, del. et lith.

Reeve, imp.

4329.

Fitch, del. et lith.

Reeve, imp.

4799.

29

1.

2.

5027.

1.

2.

W. Fitch, del. et lith.

Vincent Brooks, Imp.

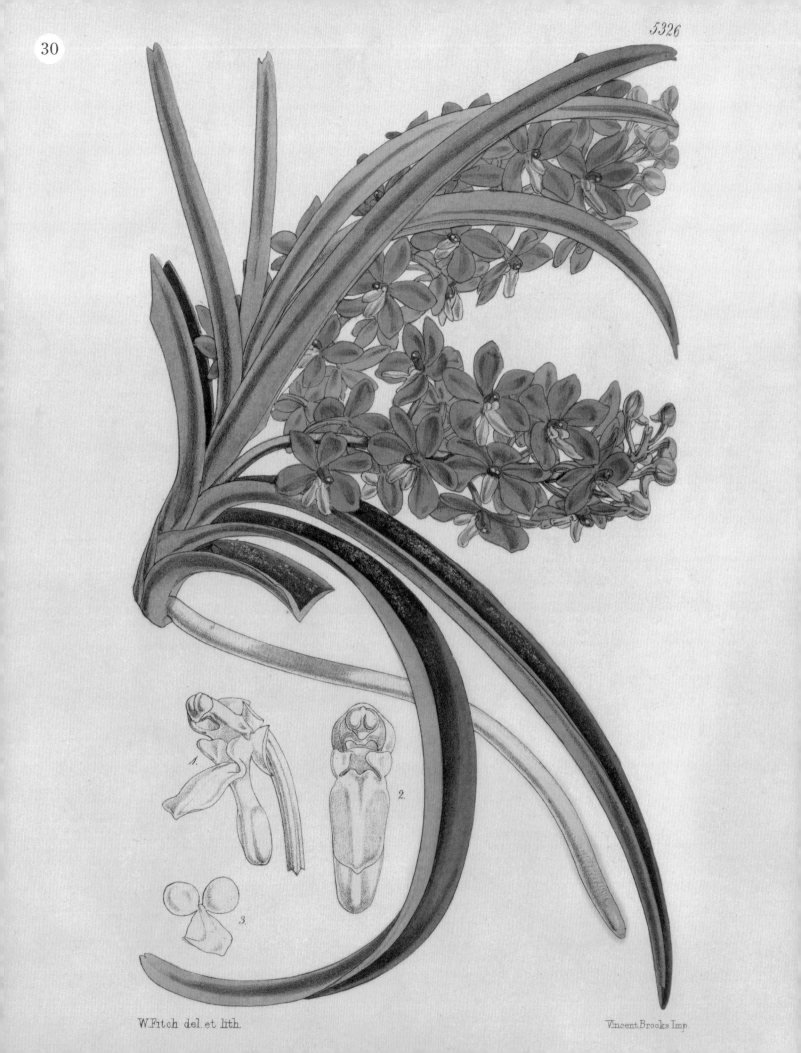

W.Fitch del. et lith.

Vincent.Brooks Imp.

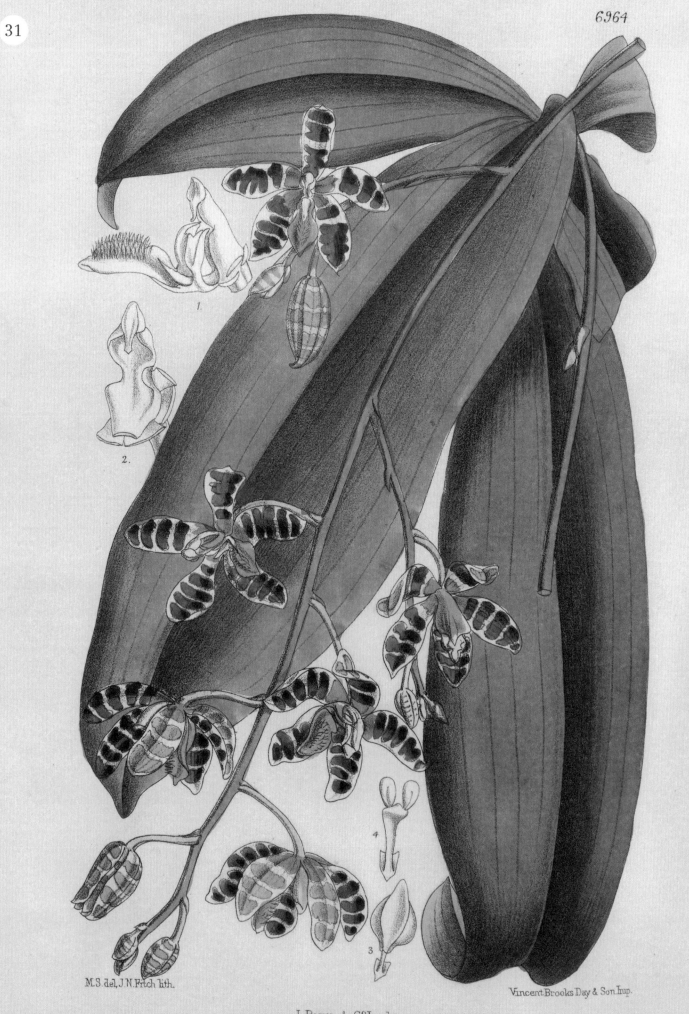

M.S.del, J.N.Fitch lith.

Vincent Brooks Day & Son Imp.

L Reeve & C° London.

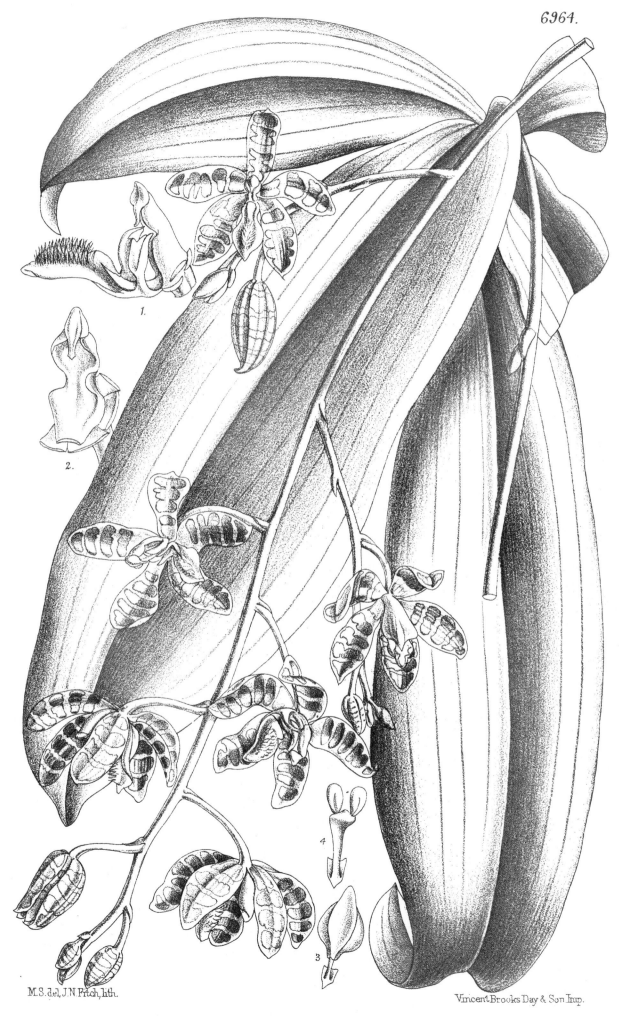

1.

2.

4

3

M.S.del, J.N Fitch, lith.

Vincent Brooks Day & Son Imp.

L Reeve & Co London.

Fitch, del et lith.

Reeve & Nichols, imp.

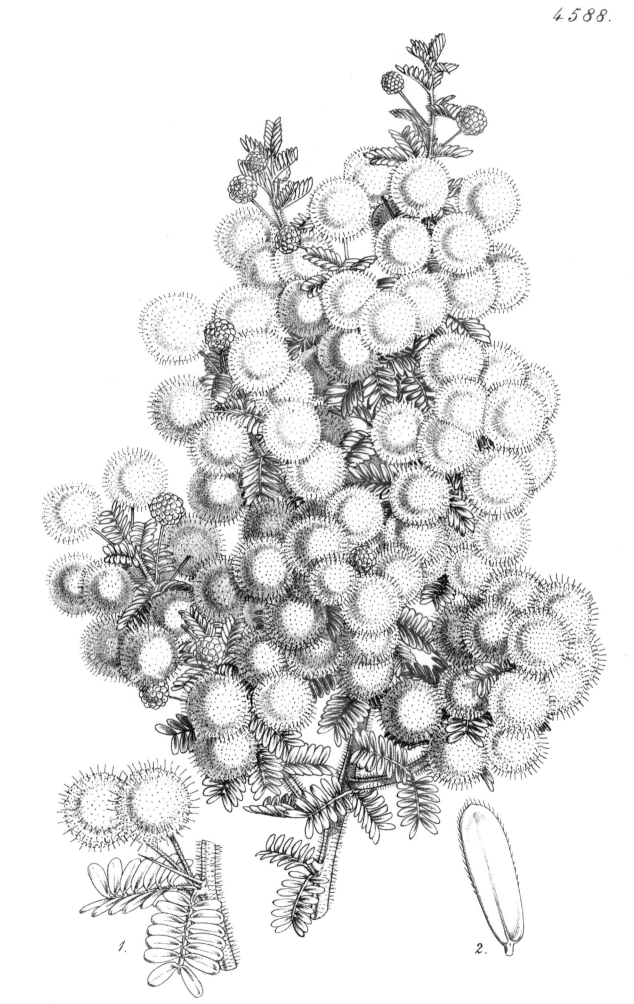

4588.

Fitch, del et lith.

Reeve & Nichols, imp.

1.

2.

1.   2.   3.

Fitch. del et lith.   Reeve, imp.

Vincent Brooks, Imp.

2

1

1.

2.

Fitch del et lith.

Reeve imp.

Fitch, del. et lith.

Reeve imp.

W. Fitch del. et lith.

Vincent Brooks Imp.

38

2.   1.

M.S.del, J.N.Fitch,lith.

Vincent Brooks Day & Son Imp

L.Reeve & Co. London.

2.

1.

M.S.del, J.N.Fitch,lith.

Vincent Brooks Day & Son,Imp.

L. Reeve & Co London

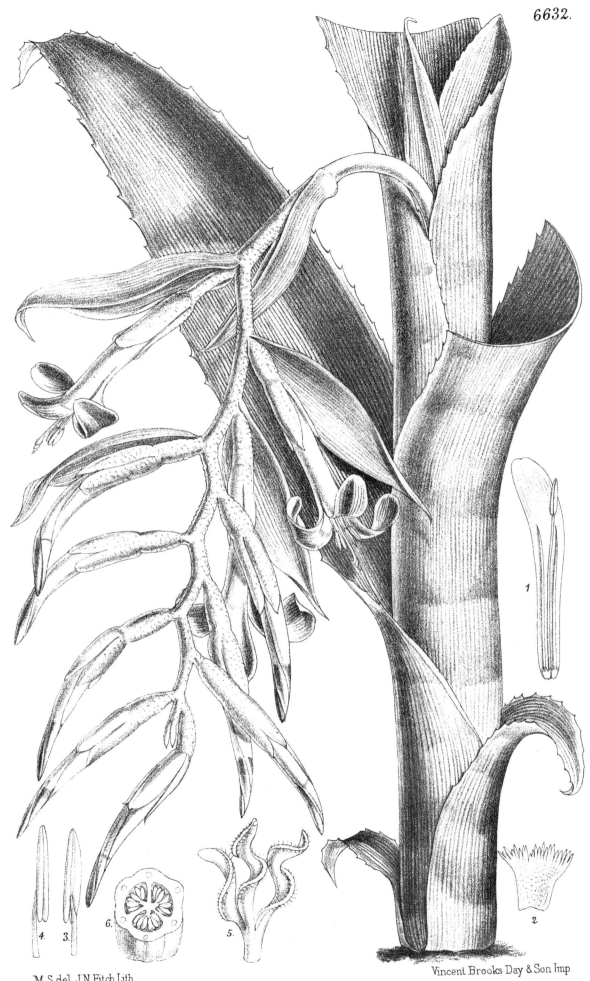

6632.

M.S.del. J.N.Fitch Lith.

Vincent Brooks Day & Son Imp

L Reeve & C⁰ London

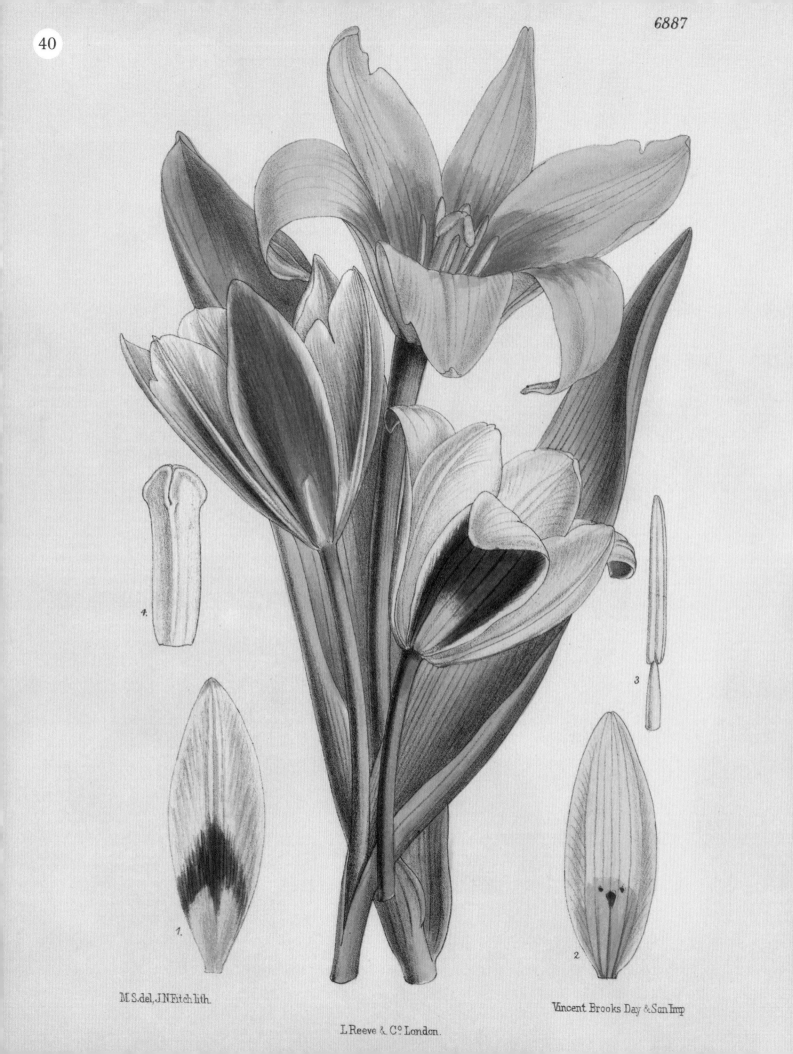

M.S.del, J.N.Fitch lith.

Vincent Brooks Day & Son Imp

L.Reeve & Cº London.

M.S.del, J.N.Fitch lith.

Vincent Brooks Day & Son Imp

L.Reeve & C.º London.

1.

Vincent Brooks Imp.

5280.

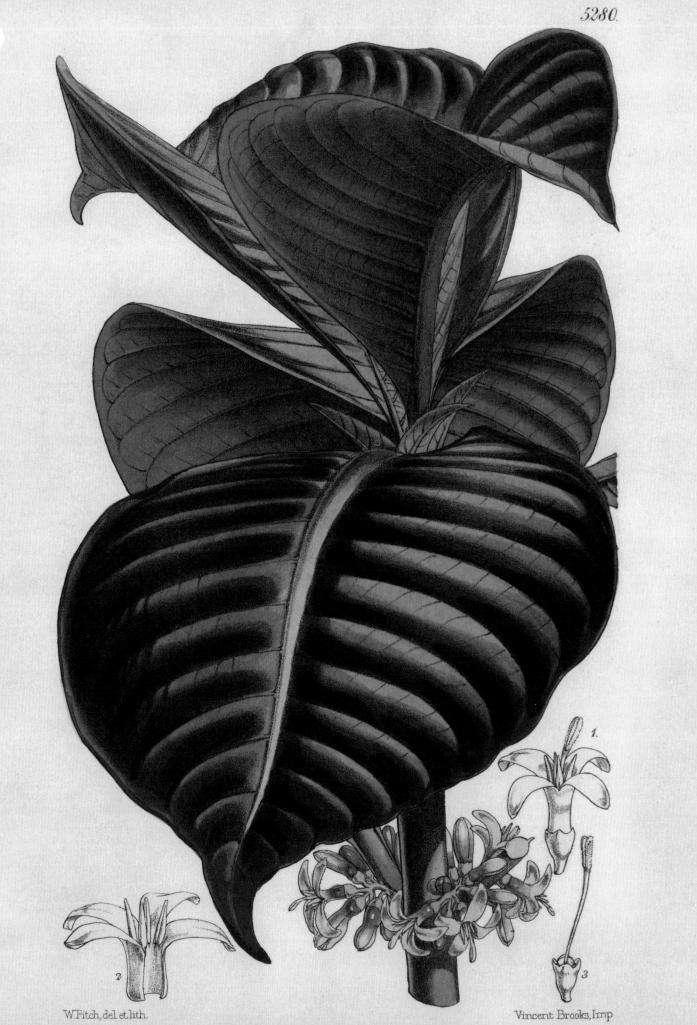

W. Fitch, del et lith.

Vincent Brooks, Imp

Vincent Brooks, Imp.

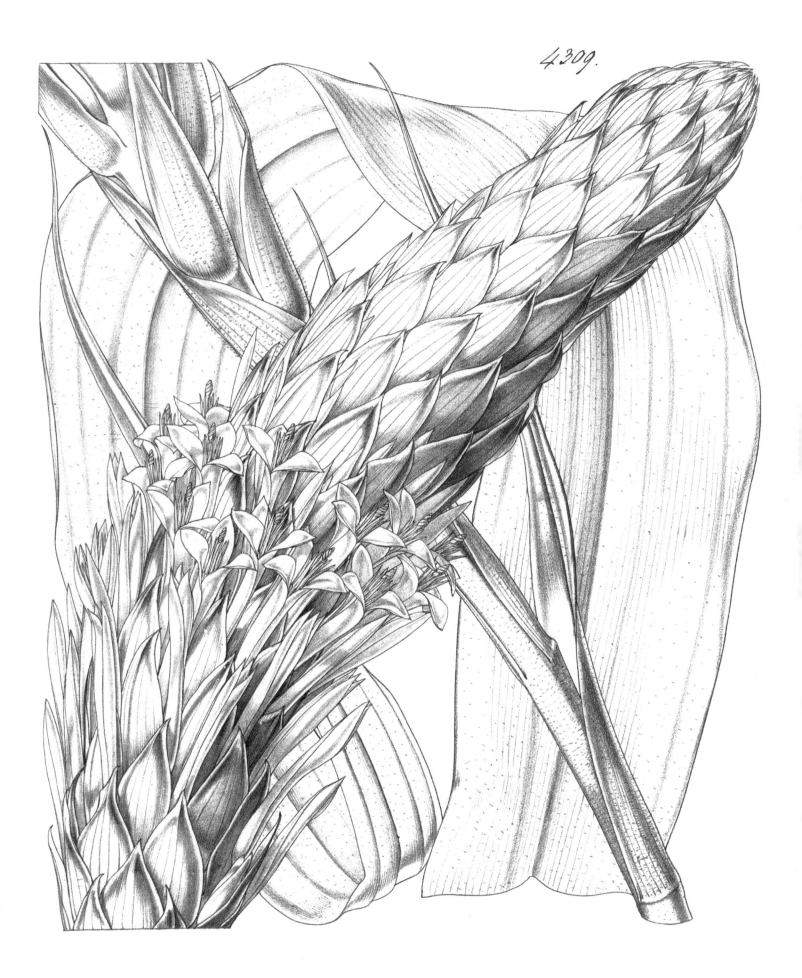

4309.